Grade 5

The Syllabus of Examinations should be read for details of requirements, especially those for scales, aural tests and sight-reading. Attention should be paid to the Special Notices on the front inside cover, where warning is given of changes.

The syllabus is obtainable from music dealers or from The Associated Board of the Royal Schools of Music, 14 Bedford Square, London WC1B 3JG (please send a stamped addressed envelope measuring about 9 × 6 ins.).

In overseas centres, information may be obtained from the Local Representative or Resident Secretary.

Requirements

SCALES AND ARPEGGIOS (from memory)

Scales

(i) in similar motion, hands together one octave apart, and each hand separately, in *all* major and minor keys (melodic *or* harmonic minor at candidate's choice) (all three octaves)

(ii) in contrary motion, both hands beginning and ending on the key-note (unison), in the keys specified in one of the following groups chosen by the candidate:
Group 1: A, F, D♭ majors and harmonic minors
Group 2: D, F♯, B♭ majors and harmonic minors
(two octaves)

Chromatic Scales

(i) in similar motion, hands together one octave apart, and each hand separately, beginning on any note named by the examiner (three octaves)

(ii) in contrary motion, both hands beginning and ending on the same note (unison), beginning on D and A♭ (two octaves)

Arpeggios

the major and minor common chords of *all* keys, in root position only, in similar motion, hands together one octave apart, and each hand separately (two octaves)

PLAYING AT SIGHT (see current syllabus)

AURAL TESTS (see current syllabus)

THREE PIECES

Candidates must prepare Nos.1 & 2 from the *same* list, A *or* B, but may choose No.3 from *either* list *or* one of the further alternatives listed below:

Schumann Abendlied (Evening Song), Op.118 No.2/3
Cui Au Berceau (In the Cradle), Op.39 No.4
These are included in More Romantic Pieces for Piano, Book III, *published by the Associated Board*

Copyright pieces in this publication are printed as issued by the copyright owners and are reproduced with their permission.

Other pieces have been checked with original source material and edited as necessary for instructional purposes. Fingering, phrasing, pedalling, metronome marks and the editorial realization of ornaments (where given) are for guidance but are not comprehensive or obligatory. Any good alternatives, which are appropriate in style, will be accepted by the examiners.

A:1
AIR in A

Edited by
Richard Jones

MATTHESON

Source: *Pièces de Clavecin* (London, 1714). Johann Mattheson, a friend of Handel, was from 1715 to 1728 Director of Music at Hamburg Cathedral. He was a fine organist and prolific writer on music as well as a composer. Apart from the first right-hand slur in bar 20, all marks of articulation are editorial suggestions only. Other editorial interventions are given in small type. Dynamics are left to the discretion of the performer. Final chords of each section may be arpeggiated.

AB 2430

A:2
SONATA in G minor
First movement

BEETHOVEN, Op.49 No.1

Source: first edition, *Deux Sonates faciles pour le Pianoforte*; Bureau d'Arts et d'Industrie, Vienna [1805]. Editorial slurs are shown by ⌢, other editorial marks are added in square brackets; in almost all cases these suggestions are offered on the basis of parallel passages elsewhere in the movement. The right-hand phrasing on the second crotchet beat of bars 30 and 51 has been added in line with bars 16ff.

A:3
RHYTHMICAL
No.6 from 'Moments at the Piano'

LUBOŠ SLUKA

No dynamics in the original; those offered here are editorial suggestions only.

Reprinted by permission, for use only in connection with the examinations of the Royal Schools of Music. All enquiries for this piece apart from the examinations should be addressed to Universal Edition (London) Ltd, 48 Great Marlborough Street, London W1V 2BN.

AB 2430

B:1
AIR
from Partita No.6 in E minor

Edited by
Walter Emery

J.S. BACH, BWV 830

Source: copy of the collected edition of all 6 Partitas published in 1731, formerly belonging to Paul Hirsch (now in the British Library) and containing manuscript alterations believed to have been authorized, if not made, by Bach. This source contains the slurs in bars 8-10, whence the editorial slur in bar 4. The editorial sharp in bar 21 is offered in comparison with the remainder of this sequence (left hand, bars 20-3).

Quavers might be lightly articulated throughout, perhaps as ♪♪♪♪ at the opening; leaping crotchets should be detached. All dynamics are editorial suggestions only.

B:2
SONATA in C
Third movement

Edited by
Howard Ferguson

HAYDN, Hob.XVI/35

Source: No.1 of *Sei Sonate . . . Opera XXX*; Artaria, Vienna 1780. Dynamics in bars 17, 22, 34, 69, 86 and 91 are original; all others are editorial suggestions only. Haydn's few marks of articulation have been applied consistently throughout the piece and incorporated into the editorial scheme. All left-hand phrasing is editorial. *Staccato* indicated by wedges in the original.

B:3
THE HARPIST

SIBELIUS, Op.34 No.8

Reprinted by permission, for use only in connection with the examinations of the Royal Schools of Music. All enquiries for this piece apart from the examinations should be addressed to Fazer Music Inc., PO Box 169, SF-02101 Espoo, Finland.

AB 2430

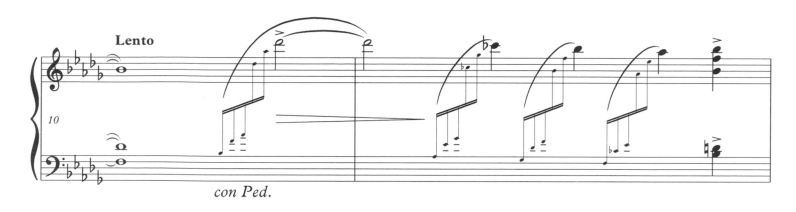

con Ped.

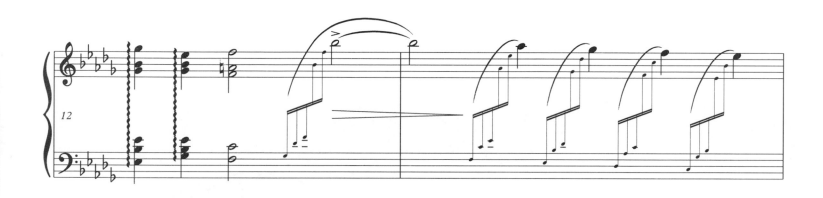

con sord.